Harry Potter™
MAGICAL
CREATURES
COLOURING BOOK

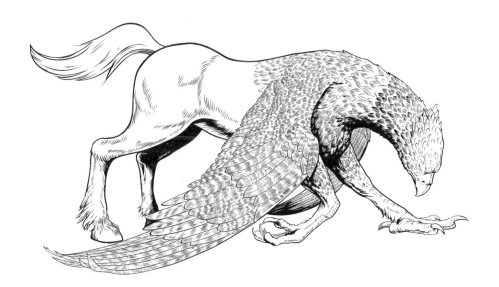

STUDIO
PRESS

An Insight Editions Book

THE CREATURES AND BEASTS

of the wizarding world are majestic and funny, chilling and loving. They are as diverse a group of characters as the students who attend Hogwarts School of Witchcraft and Wizardry, and just as much a part of the magic of the Harry Potter films. The pages that follow present a selection of the fauna from the films and invite you to reimagine the fiery red feathers of Fawkes, the ghostly hues of the merpeople, the weathered scales of dragons—and so much more.

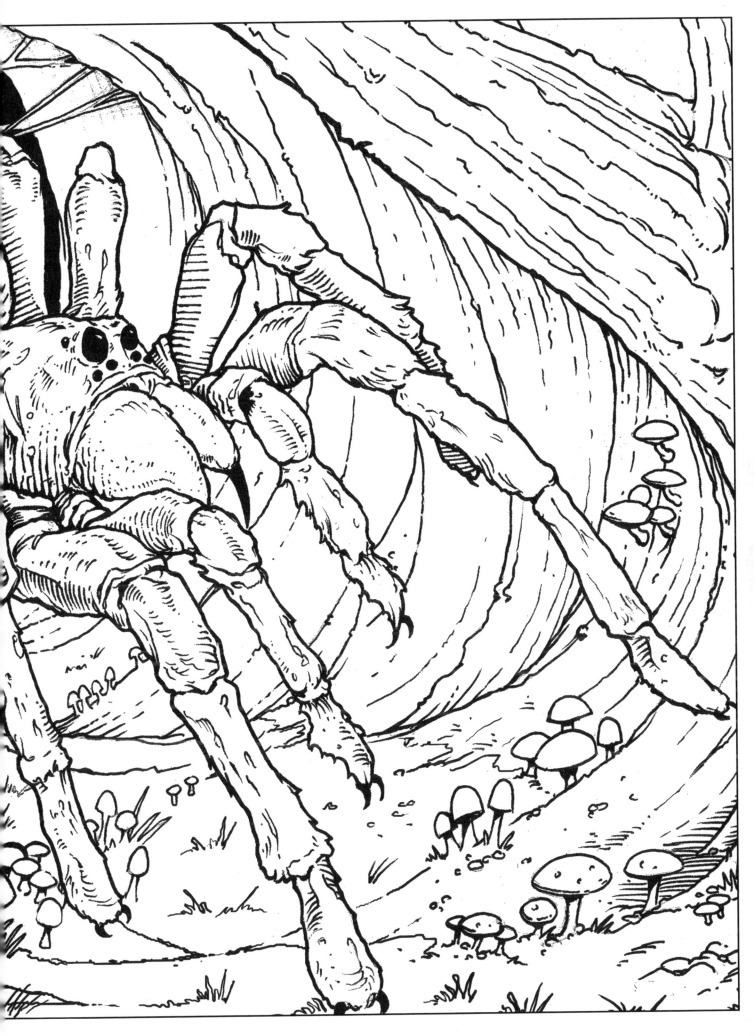

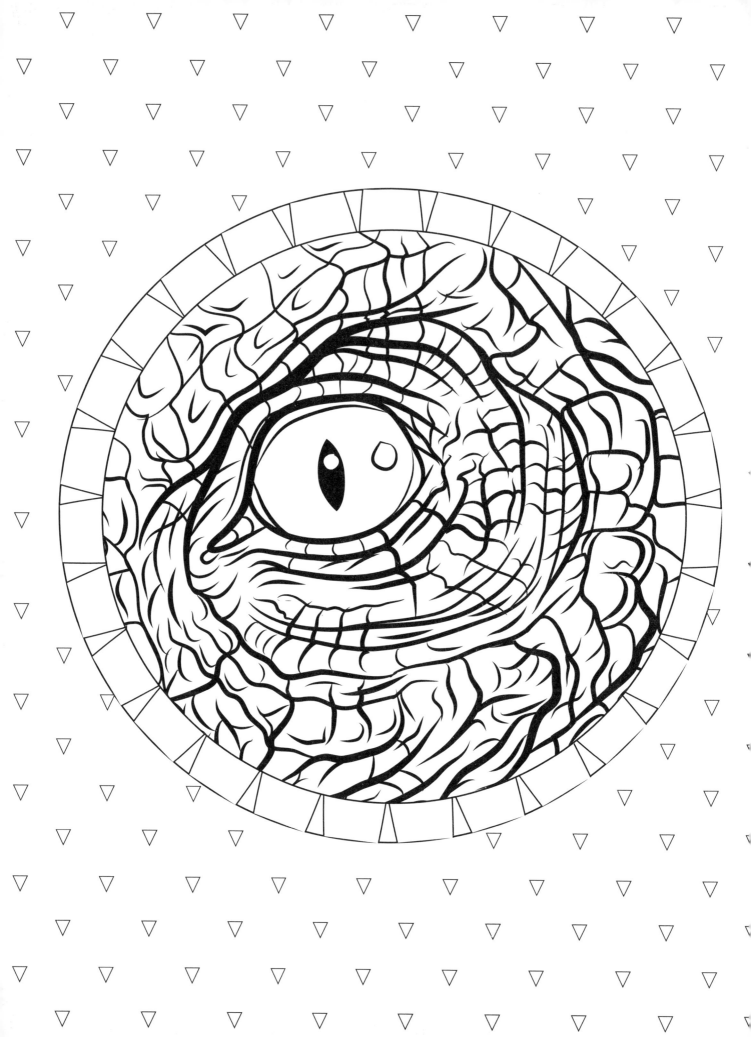

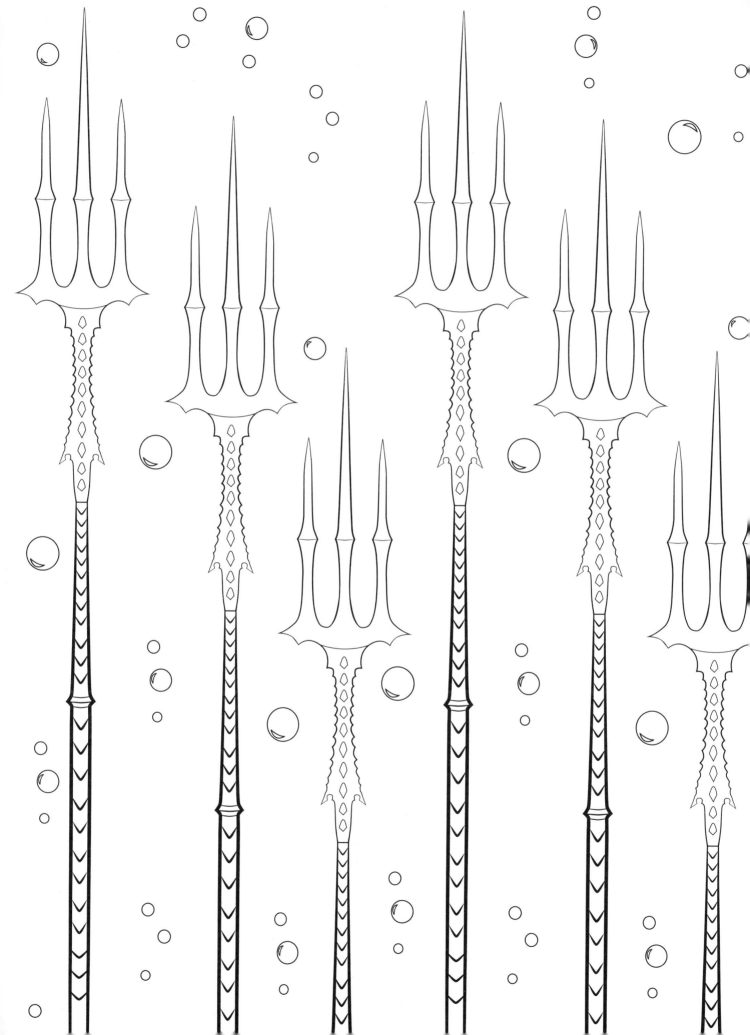

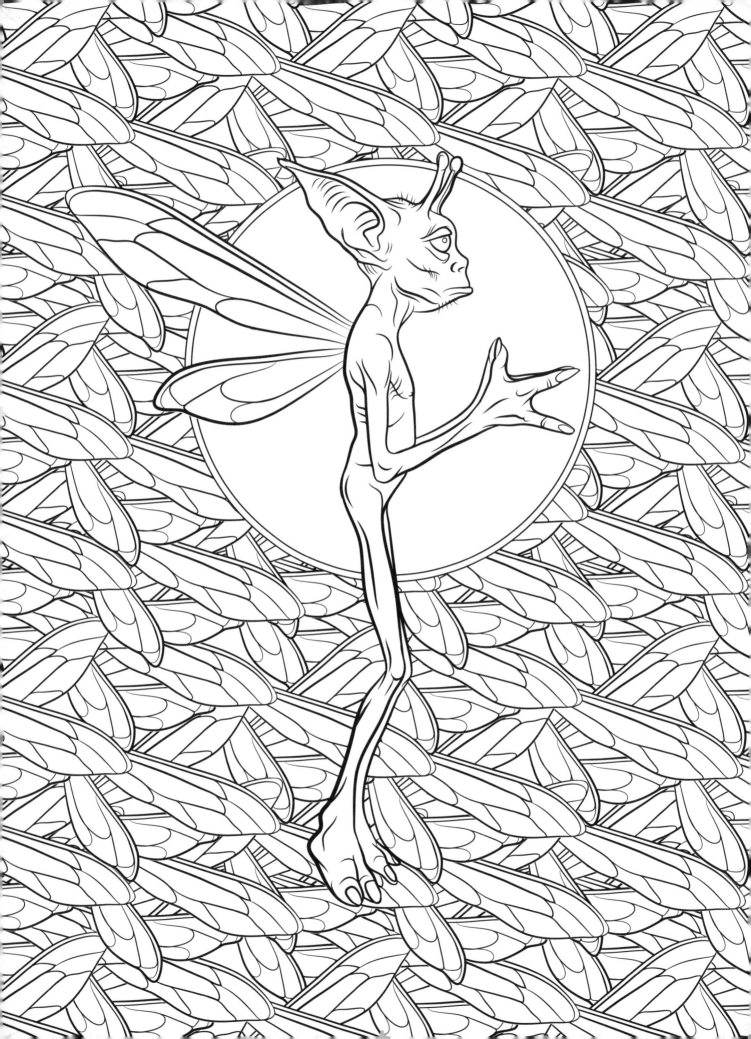

NO HAIR

HAIR

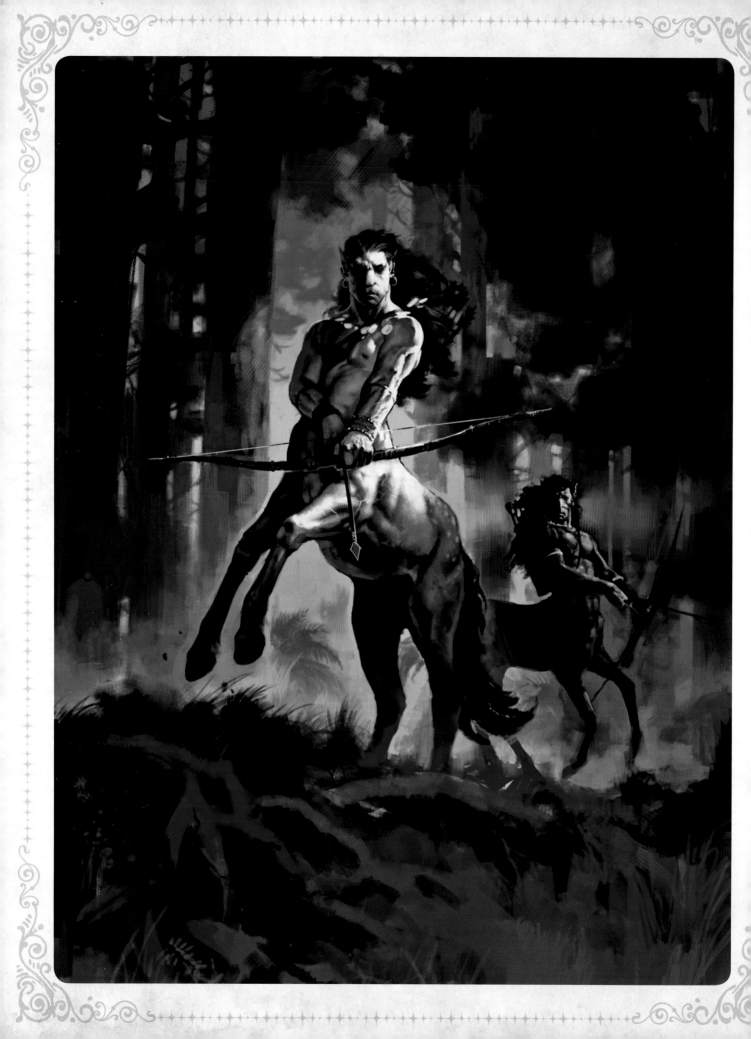

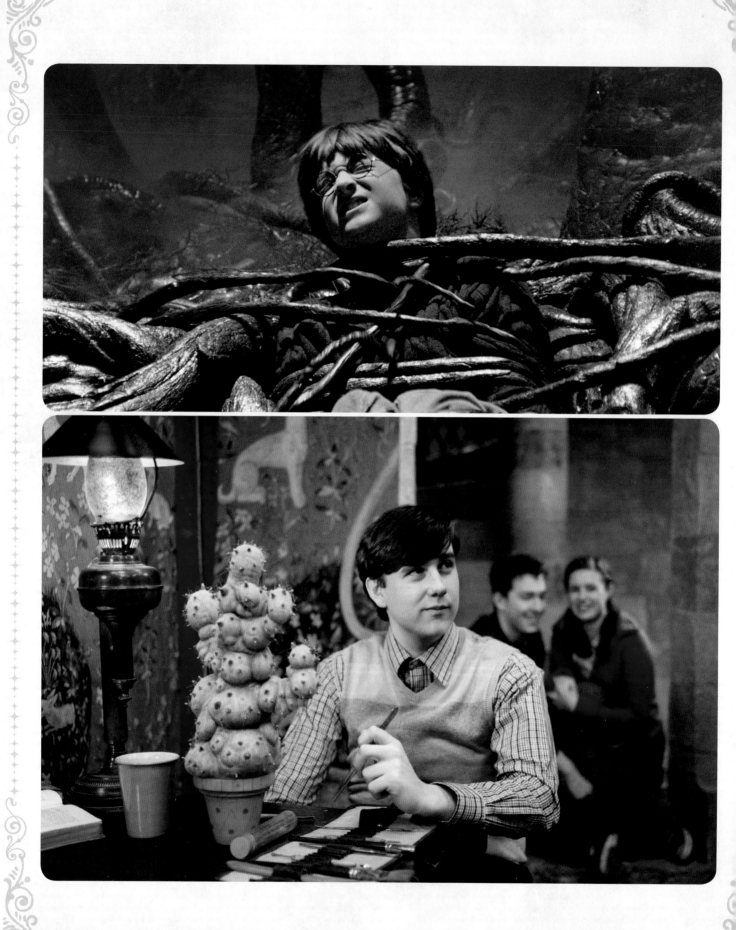

ISBN 978-1-78370-582-5

ART CREDITS:
Dumbledore, Dobby, Fawkes with Basilisk, Grawp, Battle of Hogwarts, Aragog, Lupin, and centaur concept art by Adam Brockbank. • Ukrainian Ironbelly, Hungarian Horntail, and Norbert concept art by Paul Catling. • Thestral, Pygmy Puff, Cornish Pixie, and Dirigible Plum concept art by Rob Bliss. • Whomping Willow, and Mandrake concept art by Dermot Power. • Acromantula concept art by Andrew Williamson.

Produced by

INSIGHT
EDITIONS
PO Box 3088
San Rafael, CA 94912

www.insighteditions.com

PUBLISHER: Raoul Goff
ART DIRECTOR: Chrissy Kwasnik
COVER DESIGN & LAYOUT: Jenelle Wagner
EXECUTIVE EDITOR: Vanessa Lopez
PROJECT EDITOR: Greg Solano
PRODUCTION EDITOR: Rachel Anderson
PRODUCTION MANAGER: Blake Mitchum

INSIGHT EDITIONS would like to thank Victoria Selover, Elaine Piechowski, Alix Nicholaeff, Leeana Diaz, and Melanie Swartz.

ILLUSTRATIONS BY Adam Raiti, Scott Buoncristiano, Robin F. Williams, Manuel Martinez, Maxime Lebrun, and Dee Pei.

 REPLANTED PAPER

Insight Editions, in association with Roots of Peace, will plant two trees for each tree used in the manufacturing of this book. Roots of Peace is an internationally renowned humanitarian organization dedicated to eradicating land mines worldwide and converting war-torn lands into productive farms and wildlife habitats. Roots of Peace will plant two million fruit and nut trees in Afghanistan and provide farmers there with the skills and support necessary for sustainable land use.

Manufactured in Italy by Insight Editions

10 9 8 7 6 5 4 3 2